SCAN THE CODE TO ACCESS YOUR FREE DIGITAL COPY

THIS BOOK BELONGS TO

Gwyn

EQUUS - HORSE

1. ATLAS
2. AXIS
3.
4.
5.
6.
7.
8.
9.
10.
11.
12.
13.
14.
15.
16.
17.
18.

19.
20.
21.
22.
23.
24.
25.
26.
27.
28.
29.

30.
31.
32.
33.
34.
35.
36.

EQUUS - HORSE

1. Atlas
2. Axis
3. Esophagus
4. Trachea
5. Sternocephaligus muscle
6. Scapula
7. Humerus
8. Cranial Superficial muscle
9. Heart
10. Ulna
11. Lung
12. Radius
13. Knee
14. Carpal bones
15. Cannon
16. Long pastern bone
17. Short pastern bone
18. Pedal bone
19. Liver
20. Spleen
21. Kidney
22. Large intestine
23. Tibia
24. Fibula
25. Tarsal bones
26. Splint bone
27. Cannon bone
28. Pastern bones
29. Pedal Bone
30. Vertebrae
31. Cecum
32. Small intestine
33. Stomach
34. Rectum
35. Pelvis
36. Femur

PISCIS - FISH

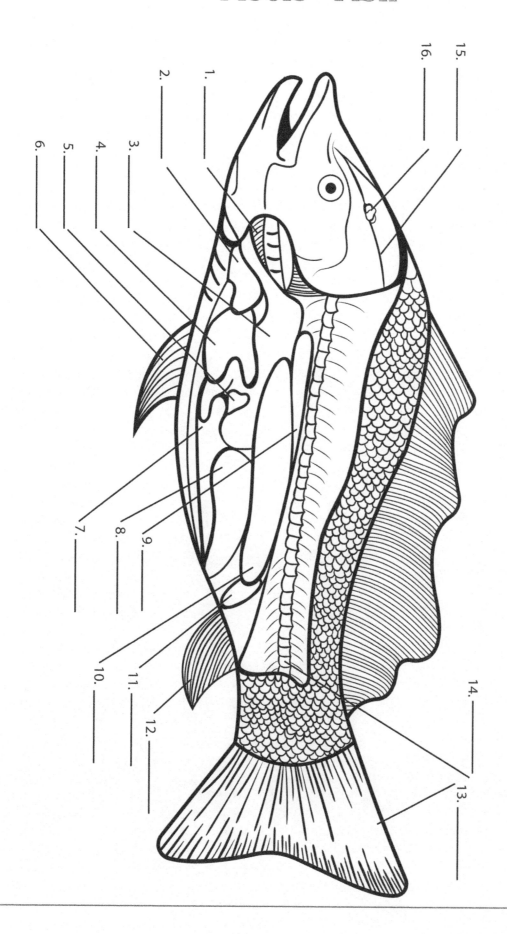

PISCIS - FISH

1.   Gill

2.   Heart

3.   Stomach

4.   Liver

5.   Spleen

6.   Pelvic fin

7.   Intestine

8.   Gonad

9.   Kidney

10.   Swim bladder

11.   Urinary bladder

12.   Anal fin

13.   Tail fin

14.   Vertebral column

15.   Spinal cord

16.   Brain

PORCUS - PIG

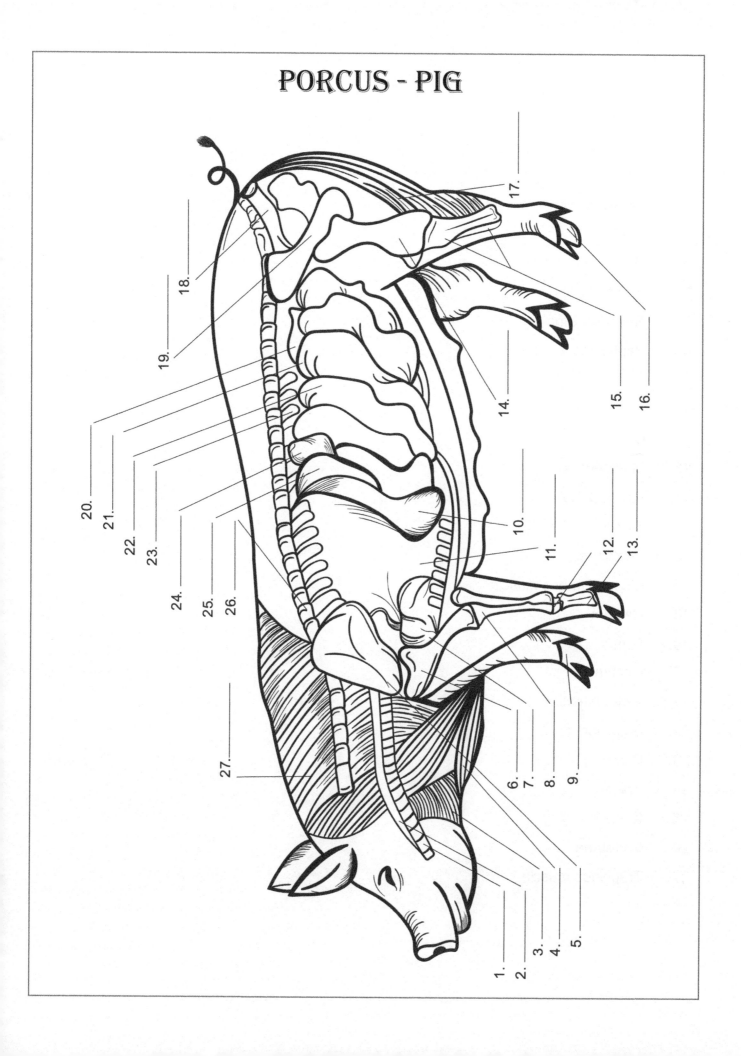

PORCUS - PIG

1. Esophagus
2. Trachea
3. Masseter muscle
4. Sternohyoideus muscle
5. Scapula
6. Humerus
7. Heart
8. Radius & Ulna
9. Phalanges
10. Liver
11. Lungs
12. Carpus
13. Metacarpus
14. Fibula & Tibia
15. Tarsus
16. Phalanges
17. Biceps femoris muscle
18. Rectum
19. Femur
20. Cecum
21. Large intestine
22. Small intestine
23. Ribs
24. Spleen
25. Kidney
26. Vertebrae
27. Trapezius muscle

PULLUM - CHICKEN

PULLUM - CHICKEN

1. Nostril
2. Larnyx
3. Trachea
4. Esophagus
5. Crop
6. Heart
7. Gall bladder
8. Proventriculus
9. Spleen
10. Liver
11. Gizzard
12. Claw
13. Pancreas
14. Duoneal loop
15. Small intestine
16. Caeca
17. Large intestine
18. Cloaca
19. Oviduct
20. Ovary
21. Kidney
22. Lungs
23. Bronchial tubes
24. Spine
25. Brain

BOS TAURUS - COW

1.
2.
3.
4.
5.
6.
7.
8.
9.
10.
11.
12.
13.
14.
15.
16.
17.
18.
19.
20.
21.
22.
23.
24.
25.
26.
27.

BOS TAURUS - COW

1. Brachiocephalicus muscle
2. Sternocephalicus muscle
3. Trachea
4. Scapula
5. Humerus
6. Heart
7. Radius & Ulna
8. Carpal joint
9. Metacarpus
10. Pastern joint
11. Liver
12. Spleen
13. Omasum
14. Tibia & Fibula
15. Metatarsus
16. Coffin joint
17. Tarsal joint
18. Femur
19. Hip joint
20. Ischium
21. Vagina
22. Rectum
23. Illium
24. Rumen
25. Esophagus
26. Ribs
27. Trapezius

TESTUDO – SEA TURTLE

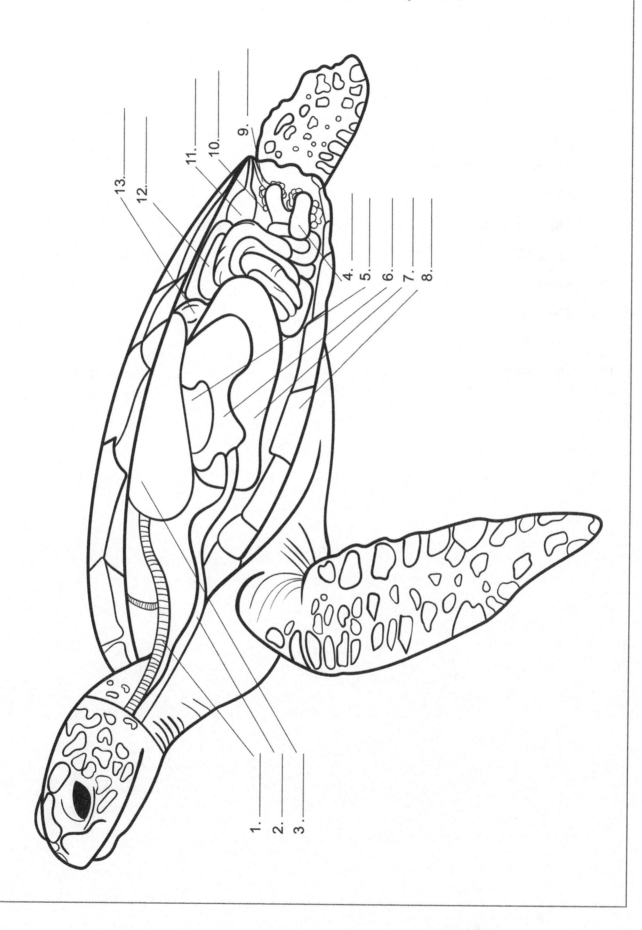

TESTUDO – SEA TURTLE

1. Trachea
2. Esophagus
3. Lung
4. Kidney
5. Heart
6. Stomach
7. Liver
8. Marginal shell
9. Oviduct
10. Ovary
11. Cloaca
12. Intestines
13. Pancreas

SELACHIMORPHA - SHARK

SELACHIMORPHA - SHARK

1. Esophagus
2. Gills
3. Cartilage
4. Fin cartilage
5. Pectoral fin support
6. Heart
7. Spleen
8. Uterus
9. Cadual fin
10. Cloaca
11. Intestine
12. Kidney
13. Liver
14. Vertebrae
15. Stomach
16. Dorsal fin

FELIS CATUS – DOMESTIC CAT

FELIS CATUS – DOMESTIC CAT

1.   Esophagus
2.   Trachea
3.   Lungs
4.   Heart
5.   Scapula
6.   Humerus
7.   Ribs
8.   Pattela
9.   Tibia & Fibula
10. Femur
11. Pelvis
12. Coccygeal Vertebrae
13. Lombar vertebrae
14. Colon
15. Intestine
16. Kidney
17. Spleen
18. Stomach
19. Liver

CANIS LUPUS FAMILIARIS – DOMESTIC DOG

CANIS LUPUS FAMILIARIS – DOMESTIC DOG

1. Sternomastoideus
2. Esophagus
3. Trachea
4. Lungs
5. Heart
6. Liver
7. Pectoralis profundus
8. Stomach
9. Intestine
10. Phalanges
11. Metatarsal bones
12. Hock Joint
13. Tibia & Fibula
14. Patella
15. Femur
16. Hip Joint
17. Kidney
18. Pelvis
19. Longissimus and Iliocostalis muscle
20. Trapezius
21. Cleidocervicalis muscle

CROCODILI - CROCODILE

1.
2.
3.
4.
5.
6.
7.
8.
9.
10.
11.
12.
13.
14.
15.
16.
17.

CROCODILI - CROCODILE

1. Spinal cord
2. Cerebellum
3. Vertebrae
4. Ribs
5. Lung
6. Esophagus
7. Trachea
8. Heart
9. Liver
10. Intestine
11. Testis
12. Spleen
13. Stomach
14. Kidney
15. Cloaca
16. Tarsus
17. Metatarsus

LEPUS - RABBIT

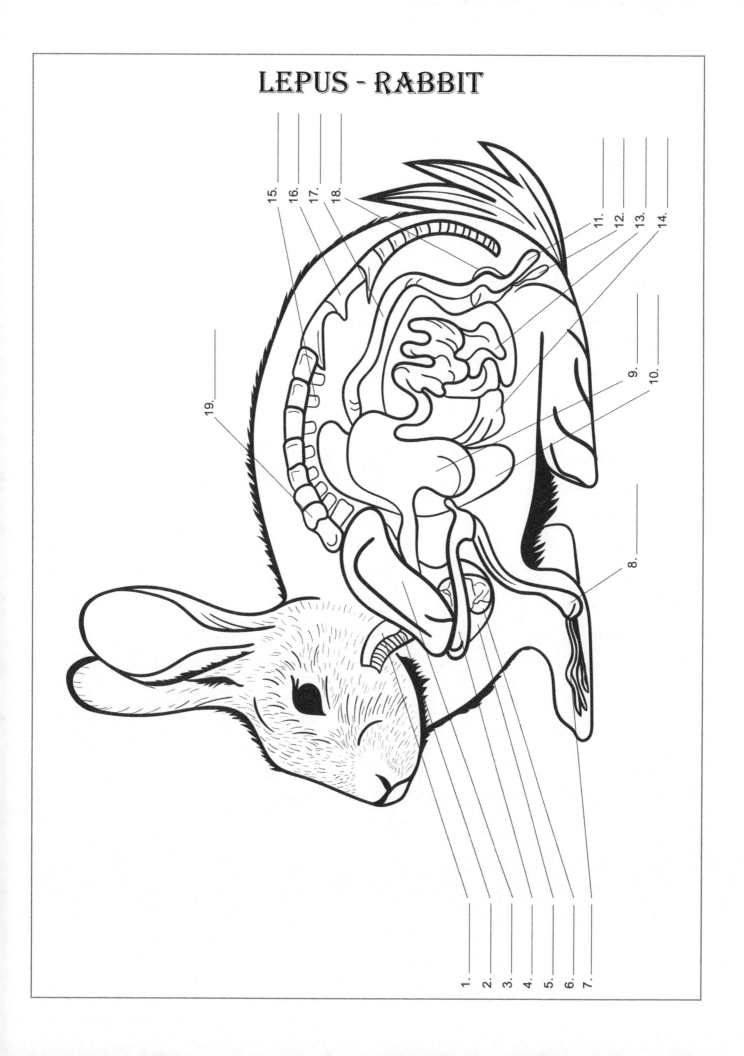

LEPUS - RABBIT

1. Esophagus
2. Trachea
3. Scapula
4. Humerus
5. Lung
6. Heart
7. Phalanges
8. Radius & Ulna
9. Stomach
10. Liver
11. Rectum
12. Urethra
13. Large Intestine
14. Appendix
15. Ribs
16. Spine
17. Small intestine
18. Bladder
19. Vertebrae

COLUMBÆ OFFERET – PIDGEON

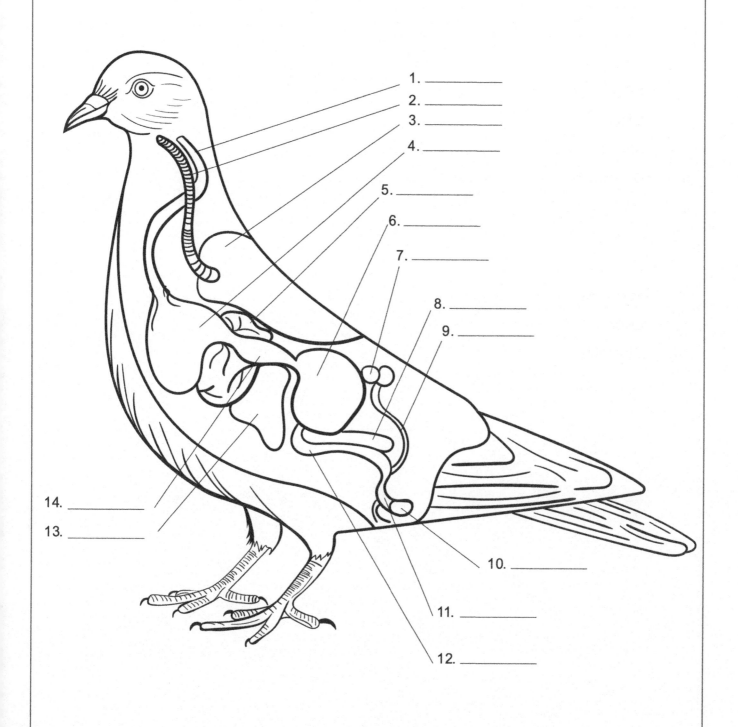

1. _____
2. _____
3. _____
4. _____
5. _____
6. _____
7. _____
8. _____
9. _____
10. _____
11. _____
12. _____
13. _____
14. _____

COLUMBÆ OFFERET - PIDGEON

1. Esophagus

2. Trachea

3. Lung

4. Crop

5. Heart

6. Gizzard

7. Kidney

8. Duodenum

9. Ureter

10. Cloaca

11. Rectum

12. Pancreas

13. Liver

14. Stomach

GIRAFFA CAMELOPARDALIS - GIRAFFE

1. _____

2. _____

3. _____

4. _____

5. _____

6. _____

7. _____

8. _____

9. _____

10. _____

11. _____

12. _____

13. _____

14. _____

15. _____

16. _____

17. _____

18. _____

GIRAFFA CAMELOPARDALIS - GIRAFFE

1. Trapezius
2. Esophagus
3. Scapula
4. Lung
5. Triceps
6. Heart
7. Humerus
8. Ulna
9. Carpus joints
10. Metacarpus
11. Phalanges
12. Vertebrae
13. Ribs
14. Ossa pelvis
15. Tibia
16. Intestine
17. Stomach
18. Patella

ELEPHANTUS - ELEPAHNT

1.
2.
3.
4.
5.
6.
7.
8.
9.
10.
11.
12.
13.
14.
15.
16.
17.
18.
19.
20.
21.
22.
23.
24.
25.
26.

ELEPHANTUS - ELEPHANT

1. Vertebrae
2. Ovary
3. Kidney
4. Crest
5. Illium
6. Sacrum
7. Pelvis
8. Hip joint
9. Femur
10. Patella
11. Tuberositas tibiae
12. Tibia & Fibula
13. Calcaneus
14. Carpals & Metacarpals & Phalanges
15. Vastus lateralis
16. External abdominal obliques
17. Pectoralis
18. Lung
19. Heart
20. Urinary bladder
21. Uterus
22. Ribs
23. Large intestine
24. Small intestine
25. Stomach
26. Spleen

SCRUTANTEM DELPHINA UIDENT - DOLPHIN

SCRUTANTEM DELPHINA UIDENT - DOLPHIN

1. Dorsal fin
2. Spinal column
3. Stomach
4. Kidney
5. Anus
6. Urogenital slit
7. Pelvis
8. Fluke
9. Flipper
10. Intestine
11. Liver
12. Rib
13. Heart
14. Pectoral flipper
15. Humerus & Radius
16. Lung
17. Scapula
18. Rostrum

OVIUM - SHEEP

1.
2.
3.
4.
5.
6.
7.
8.
9.
10.
11.
12.
13.
14.
15.
16.
17.
18.
19.
20.

OVIUM - SHEEP

1. Scapula
2. Vertebral column
3. Ribs
4. Spleen
5. Dorsal sac of rumen
6. Sacroiliac joint
7. Hip joint
8. Femur
9. Patella
10. Tarsal bones
11. Metatarsal bones
12. Phalanges
13. Abomasum
14. Ventral sac of rumen
15. Intestines
16. Esophagus
17. Trachea
18. Lung
19. Humerus
20. Heart

CAPRA - GOAT

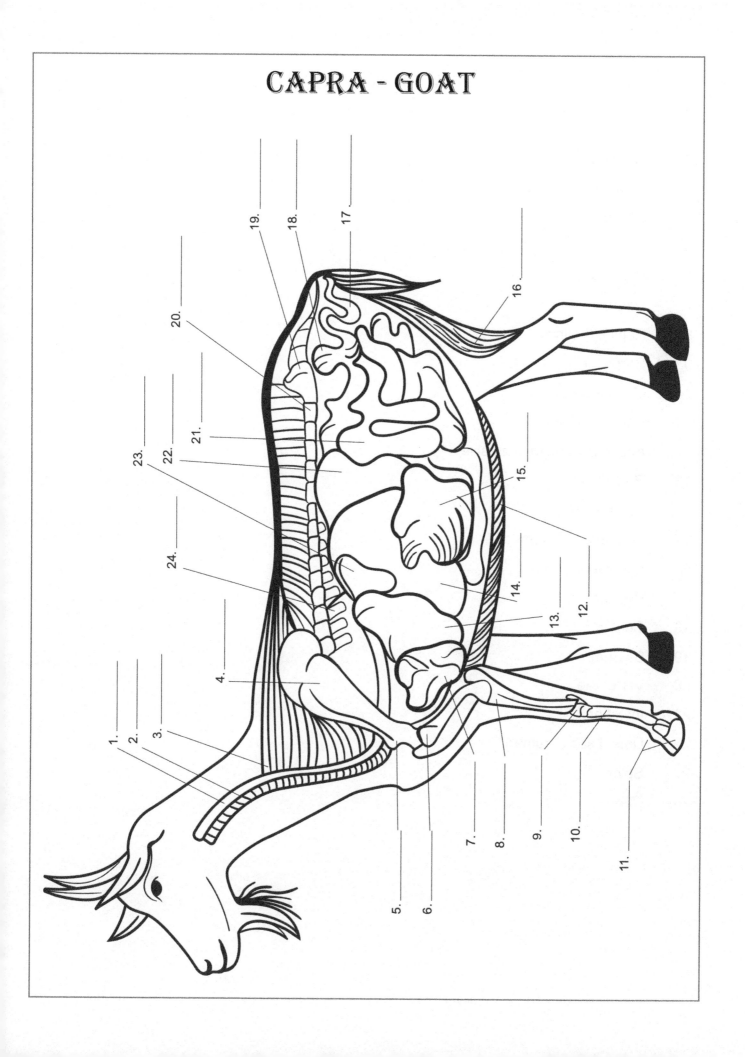

CAPRA - GOAT

1. Esophagus
2. Trachea
3. Trapezius muscle
4. Scapula
5. Acromion
6. Humerus
7. Heart
8. Radius & Ulna
9. Carpal bones
10. Metacarpals
11. Bones of digits
12. Ascending pectoral muscle
13. Reticulum
14. Abomasum
15. Ventral sac of rumen
16. Peroneus longus
17. Rectum
18. Cecum
19. Sacrum
20. Vertebrae
21. Intestine
22. Dorsal sac of rumen
23. Spleen
24. Ribs

MUS - RAT

1.

2.

3.

4.

5.

6.

7.

8.

9.

10.

11.

12.

13.

14.

15.

16.

MUS - RAT

1. Spinal cord
2. Lung
3. Stomach
4. Spleen
5. Kidney
6. Large intestine
7. Small intestine
8. Caecum
9. Bladder
10. Preputial gland
11. Biceps femoris
12. External oblique
13. Liver
14. Biceps brachii
15. Heart
16. Trachea

SPHENISCIDAE - PENGUIN

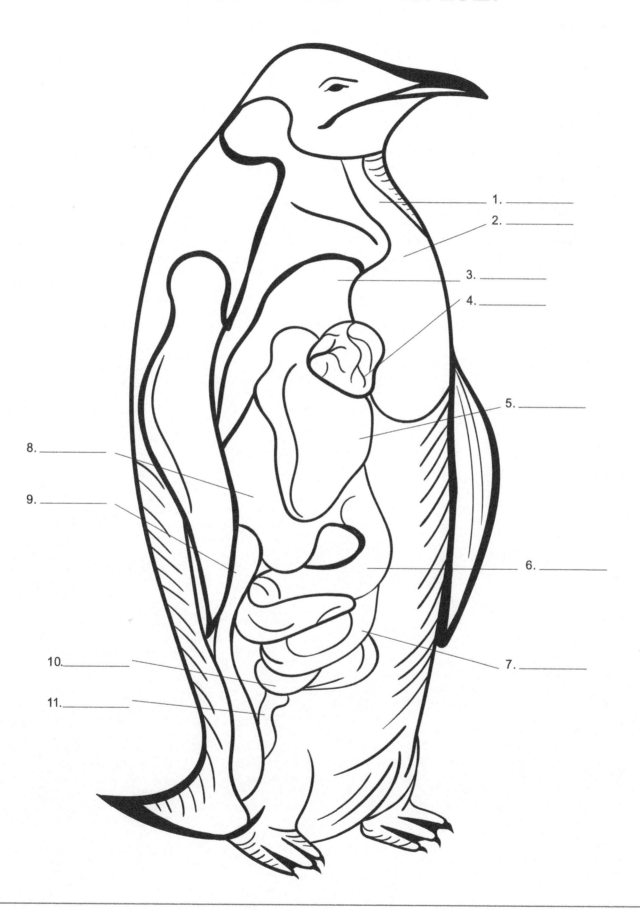

1. _____

2. _____

3. _____

4. _____

5. _____

6. _____

7. _____

8. _____

9. _____

10. _____

11. _____

SPHENISCIDAE - PENGUIN

1. Esophagus

2. Crop

3. Lung

4. Heart

5. Liver

6. Stomach

7. Small intestine

8. Gizzard

9. Kidney

10. Cloaca

11. Rectum

SIGILLUM – SEAL

SIGILLUM - SEAL

1. Esophagus

2. Trachea

3. Lung

4. Stomach

5. Kidney

6. Large intestine

7. Pelvis

8. Bladder

9. Anus

10. Swimming muscle

11. Small intestine

12. Liver

13. Heart

RANAE - FROG

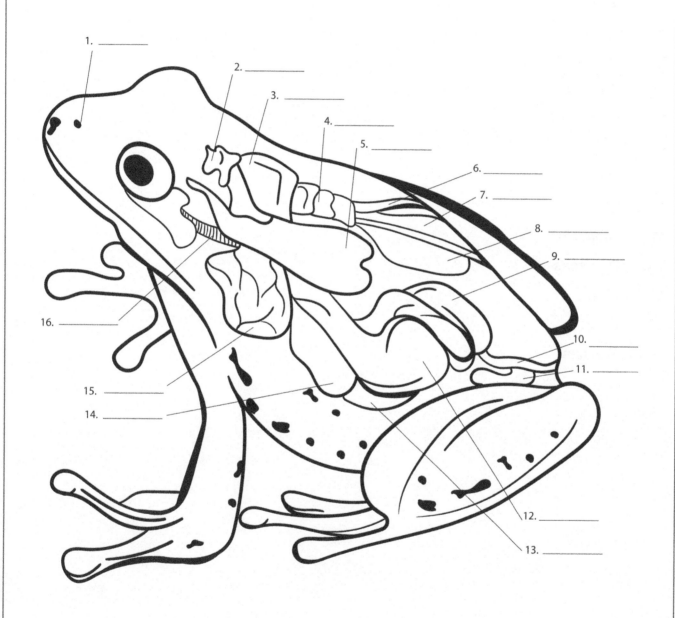

1. _____

2. _____

3. _____

4. _____

5. _____

6. _____

7. _____

8. _____

9. _____

10. _____

11. _____

12. _____

13. _____

14. _____

15. _____

16. _____

RANAE - FROG

1. External nares
2. Atlas
3. Scapula
4. Vertebrae
5. Lung
6. Urostyle
7. Sacrum
8. Kidney
9. Intestine
10. Cloaca
11. Bladder
12. Stomach
13. Pancreas
14. Liver
15. Heart
16. Trachea

ANGUIS - SERPENTINE

1. _____
2. _____
3. _____
4. _____

5. _____
6. _____
7. _____
8. _____

11. _____
12. _____
13. _____

9. _____
10. _____

14. _____
15. _____

16. _____

ANGUIS - SERPENTINE

1. Vertebrae
2. Ribs
3. Trachea
4. Esophagus
5. Lungs
6. Heart
7. Stomach
8. Liver
9. Pancreas
10. Gallbladder
11. Large intestine
12. Small intestine
13. Kidney
14. Rectum
15. Testes
16. Cloaca

URSA - BEAR

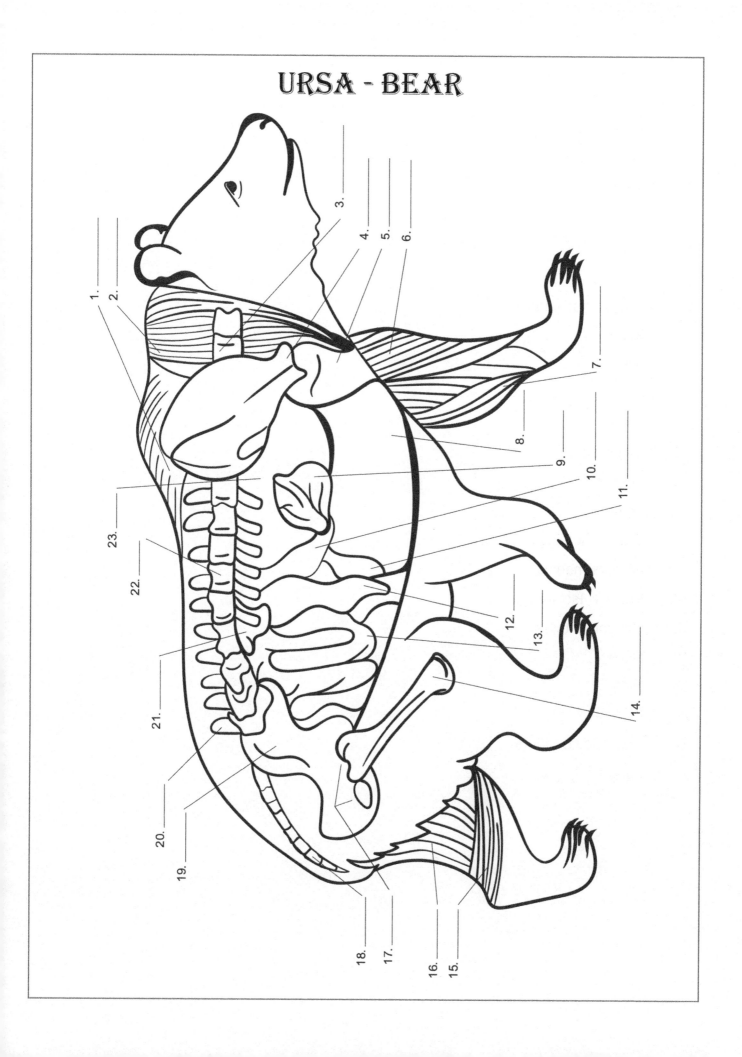

URSA - BEAR

1. Trapezius
2. Cephalohumeral
3. Cervical vertebrae
4. Scapula
5. Humerus
6. Extensor carpi radialis
7. Flexor carpi ulnaris
8. Stomach
9. Heart
10. Liver
11. Spleen
12. Diaphragm
13. Intestine
14. Femur
15. Gastrocnemius
16. Gluteus medius
17. Pelvis & Ischium
18. Caudal vertebrae
19. Illium
20. Ribs
21. Kidney
22. Thoracic vertebrae
23. Lung

SIMIA - MONKEY

10.
11.
12.
13.
14.
15.
16.
17.
18.
19.
20.

1.
2.
3.
4.
5.
6.
7.
8.
9.
21.

SIMIA - MONKEY

1. Esophagus
2. Clavicle
3. Humerus
4. Lungs
5. Heart
6. Stomach
7. Spleen
8. Large intestine
9. Bladder
10. Deltoid
11. Pectorals
12. Arm flexors
13. Liver
14. Extensors muscle
15. Flexors muscle
16. Small intestine
17. Cecum
18. Ovary
19. Urethra
20. Femur
21. Radius & Ulna

INAMABILIS SCIURUS - SQUIRREL

INAMABILIS SCIURUS - SQUIRREL

1. Phalanges
2. Carpals & Metacarpals
3. Radius & Ulna
4. Humerus
5. Tibia & Fibula
6. Femur
7. Ischium
8. Caudal vertebrae
9. Urethra
10. Large intestine
11. Small intestine
12. Kidney
13. Liver
14. Stomach
15. Ribs
16. Vertebrae
17. Heart
18. Lung
19. Scapula

Made in the USA
Monee, IL
09 December 2023

48668371R00031